HEINEMANN GUIDED READERS
ELEMENTARY LEVEL

ROBERT C. O'BRIEN

Z for Zachariah

Retold by Peter Hodson

Illustrated by Jerry Hoare

D0939899

HEINEMANN

ELEMENTARY LEVEL

Series Editor: John Milne

The Heinemann Guided Readers provide a choice of enjoyable reading material for learners of English. The series is published at five levels – Starter, Beginner, Elementary, Intermediate and Upper. At **Elementary Level**, the control of content and language has the following main features:

Information Control

Stories have straightforward plots and a restricted number of main characters. Information which is vital to the understanding of the story is clearly presented and repeated when necessary. Difficult allusion and metaphor are avoided and cultural backgrounds are made explicit.

Structure Control

Students will meet those grammatical features which they have already been taught in their elementary course of studies. Other grammatical features occasionally occur with which the students may not be so familiar, but their use is made clear through context and reinforcement. This ensures that the reading as well as being enjoyable provides a continual learning situation for the students. Sentences are kept short – a maximum of two clauses in nearly all cases – and within sentences there is a balanced use of simple adverbial and adjectival phrases. Great care is taken with pronoun reference.

Vocabulary Control

At **Elementary Level** there is a limited use of a carefully controlled vocabulary of approximately 1,100 basic words. At the same time, students are given some opportunity to meet new or unfamiliar words in contexts where their meaning is obvious. The meaning of words introduced in this way is reinforced by repetition. Help is also given to the students in the form of vivid illustrations which are closely related to the text.

Contents

Introduction

The war only lasted a week, but it was terrible. Nuclear bombs exploded and killed millions of people.

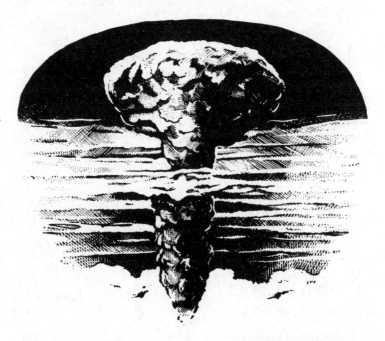

Some people did not die at once. But these people had no protection against the radiation. They all had radiation sickness. Soon they became very ill. Then, they died. Radioactive pollution killed all the people, animals, birds, trees and grass.

The water in the rivers is polluted. The radioactive world is dead and silent. But somewhere, someone is alive and well . . .

1

My Valley

My name's Ann – Ann Burden. I'm American. I was fifteen years old when the war started. Now, I'm nearly sixteen.

I'm the only person alive after the war. I live in a valley in the Middle West of the United States. I'm lucky. The bombs and radioactivity did not fall in my valley. It is green. The trees have leaves. I can drink the water in one of the streams.

I live on a farm. It was my parents' farm, but my parents are dead. They left our valley soon after the war. They went to look for other people outside the valley, but they never came back. The radioactivity killed them.

In my valley, the cows can eat the green grass. The birds sing in the trees. The air is clean. The sun shines in the blue,

summer sky. But outside the valley, everything is dead and radioactive. Nothing can live.

I'm alone in the world. Or is there somebody else?

2

I See Someone

After the bombs exploded, the telephones didn't work. My father went to the nearest town – Ogdentown. He took my brother, Joseph, and my cousin, David, with him. My mother stayed with me. She was very worried. She was afraid of the radioactivity.

When my father came back, it was night.

'What did you find?' said my mother to my father.

'Bodies,' he said, 'dead bodies. All our friends are dead.'

The next day, all the family went to another town – Dean Town. This time, my mother went too. She wanted to be with my father. Our neighbours, Mr and Mrs Klein, went with them.

I stayed at the farm. There was a lot of work to do.

'Joseph,' said my father. 'You stay with Ann. Help her look after the animals.'

But Joseph didn't want to stay. He hid in Mr Klein's truck. The trucks left the valley. They didn't come back. I think the radioactivity killed everybody.

Today, it is 20th May. My family left the valley in April last year. I've been alone for a year. I haven't seen anyone for a year. I haven't spoken to anyone for a year. There's nothing on the radio now. I remember the last words on the radio. The man was speaking from Boston.

'There are only a few people alive here,' he said. 'We have eaten all our food. Everything is radioactive. We are hungry. We are all going to die.'

The next day, the radio was silent.

I'm afraid. I think someone is coming. I've been alone for a long time. I don't want to see anybody now.

I've seen smoke in the sky to the north. I've seen the smoke three times. I climbed the hill at the end of the valley.

The smoke came from a fire. I saw the fire through my father's binoculars. Each day, the smoke gets nearer. Someone is lighting a fire every day. Someone is coming towards my valley.

Who?

3

Someone is Coming

The smoke is now very near. The fire is always near the road. The road leads to my valley. Someone is walking towards me. Someone will see me soon. Is it a man or a woman? Perhaps there are two people.

I'm writing this in my notebook. I got the notebook from Mr Klein's store in February. I also took some pens. I write something every day. I write about my life, about the weather and about the farm. Soon, I'll write about this other person too. But what will I say?

Yes, it's true. I'm not the only person in the world! I'm excited, but I'm afraid too.

In my valley, I have enough food. There are cows and chickens on the farm. I have fresh milk and fresh eggs. I can get clothes and many other things from Mr Klein's store. I'm free now. But what is this other person like? Kind or cruel?

I don't like living alone. But I don't want to live with a cruel person. I'll keep my gun near me. I don't like guns, but I'll be safe with a gun. I'll put some food and clothes in a secret place. It's a cave in the hill. Perhaps I will want to hide there . . .

———

24th May. I've seen the other person, through the binoculars. It's a man. He looks strange. He's wearing a green suit. The suit is strange. It covers his head, his body, his arms, hands,

legs and feet. He has a plastic case on his back. He is coming towards my valley.

The man is pulling something. It's a wagon – a large box on two wheels. The wagon has a green cover. When he leaves the radioactive land, he will be in my valley!

4

The Man in the Green Suit

It is night. I'm in the cave in the hill. I'm hiding. I think the man is in my house. I'm not sure. It is dark and I can't see clearly.

The man doesn't know where I am. He hasn't seen me. I'm hiding from him. I want to watch him. I want to see how he lives.

When he first saw the valley, he stopped walking. He saw the river, the house and fields. He saw that the trees and grass were green.

He was very happy. He ran to a tree and stood by it. But he didn't take off his suit. He picked some leaves from the tree. He looked at the leaves through the glass covering his face.

Then he ran back to his wagon. He took out an instrument and tested the air. Yes, the air was safe!

He went back to the wagon and took out a Geiger counter. Then he walked slowly up the road. He was testing my valley. Was there radiation here? He listened carefully to the instrument.

Yes, the valley was safe.

He stopped walking and took off his mask.

'Is anyone here?' he shouted.

I didn't reply. I wanted to talk to him, but I was afraid.

The man has a beard. His hair is long and dark brown and his face is thin and white.

He went back to the wagon again. He put his instruments away and took out a gun. Then he moved towards the house.

He didn't go into the house. He walked slowly round it. Perhaps he was afraid. He looked in through the windows. Then he went to the door.

'Is anyone here?' he shouted again.

I didn't answer..

After a few minutes, he went into the house. Twenty minutes later, he came out. It was getting dark. He went back to his wagon. He opened the green, plastic cover and took out a tent.

Soon, he had cooked a meal on a fire near his tent. He didn't go into the house to sleep. He stayed in his tent.

Who is he?

I'm watching him, carefully. Shall I speak to him? I don't know. I'm afraid.

_____

25th May. I woke up early. I came out of the cave, quietly and carefully. The man was awake, but he didn't see me. He was carrying his gun and his Geiger counter. He was wearing his green, plastic suit. He walked behind the house. He was going towards my chickens! I heard the gun go off. Bang!

The man came back with a dead chicken. One of my chickens! He put the chicken down on top of the wagon. Then he walked away towards the church and the store. I watched him through my binoculars.

13

The cows in the field saw him. They were frightened and ran away. Then he saw the water in the pond. He took his Geiger counter and held it close to the water. Then he put it in the water. Safe! He was pleased and drank some.

Next, he went to the store. He tested it with his Geiger counter and went in. A few minutes later, he came out with some tins of food.

The sky was blue and the sun was very hot. It was nearly eleven o'clock. He looked at the water in Burden Creek. Then he made a terrible mistake. He forgot to test the water!

He took off his plastic suit and clothes and jumped into the water. He stayed in the water a long time. But I know the water in Burden Creek is dangerous. There are no fish in the water. The grass near the Creek is dead.

5

Faro the Dog

This afternoon, a strange thing happened. My brother's dog, Faro, came back. He looks terrible. He's very, very thin. Perhaps Faro was living near the trees at the end of the valley.

Faro moved quietly towards the house. The man was cooking the chicken on a fire. He wasn't wearing his plastic suit. Faro stopped a few metres from him. The man saw the dog and called him. But Faro didn't go near the man. He waited.

When the chicken was cooked, the man gave some to Faro. Faro ate the chicken, very quickly. Then he ran off. He came up the hill and found me. I'm worried. Perhaps Faro will show the man my secret cave.

The man is bigger and stronger than I am. I don't want him to find me. While I'm in my cave, I'm free.

———

26th May. It's Sunday. I know the date, because I have a calendar in the cave. I have a clock too.

On Sundays, before the war, I always went to church with my parents. After they died, I went to church alone. But today, I'm not going to church. I'm going to watch the man.

The man got up early and cooked his breakfast. He left some meat for Faro.

After breakfast, Faro went to the store with the man. The man walked quickly. He wasn't wearing his plastic suit.

When he came out of the store, he looked different. He was wearing new clothes. He had cut his hair and his beard. He looks kinder now. I think he is about thirty years old.

He walked down the road, towards the south end of the

valley. He looked at everything as he went. He saw the small stream, then the pond and the other stream in Burden Creek. He stopped. There were two streams! He had only tested one stream.

He walked on to the place where the two streams come together. He sat and looked. One stream is full of fish. Nothing is living in the other stream. I know the man is worried. He looked and looked at the water.

A few minutes later, he got up and walked to the end of the valley. He stood near the trees and looked into the radioactive land. Behind him were the trees and the grass of my valley. In front were the radioactive rocks and dust.

He stood there for about twenty minutes. Then he turned and walked slowly back towards the house.

About half-way to the house, he stopped. He sat down in the road and was very sick. He was sick again, three times, before he got to his tent. When he got to the tent, he went inside. He hasn't come out again.

6

Radiation Sickness

27th May. It's morning. I've eaten my breakfast. I'm sitting outside the cave. I'm looking at the man's tent, through my binoculars.

Faro, the dog, is hungry this morning. The man didn't feed him. He hasn't come out of the tent. I think he is sick. Will the man die?

Now it is late afternoon. The man is in the tent. I must help him. I'll go and see him, but I'll take my gun with me. Perhaps he'll be dangerous.

28th May. I'm back in the house – in my bedroom. The man is in the tent. He sleeps most of the time. He's so sick that he can't get up.

Yesterday, I looked inside the tent. The man was asleep. His eyes were closed. He had been sick. He was breathing quickly. Near him, there was a green, plastic water-bottle. He had knocked it over.

I went inside the tent. The smell was terrible. I touched the man's hand. It was dry and hot.

'Edward,' said the man. 'Edward?'

The man wasn't looking at me, but he saw my gun. He said

something but I didn't understand. He closed his eyes again.

'You're sick,' I said. 'You're very ill.'

He spoke again. 'Water. Please give me water,' he said.

'All right,' I said. 'I'll get you some water. It will take a few minutes.'

I ran into the house and got a cup. Then I went to the stream for some water. When I got to the tent, the man was asleep. I touched him on the arm and woke him.

'Here,' I said. 'Drink this.'

He was too ill to sit up. He tried to drink from the cup, but he dropped it. I held his head and gave him the cup again. He was very thirsty and drank the water quickly.

'More,' he said. 'More water.'

'Not now,' I said. 'It'll make you sick again.'

The man went to sleep again.

I got a cloth and cleaned his face. Then, I gave him a blanket.

A few hours later, I made some soup. I took it to him in the tent. I was surprised. He was awake. He looked at me. Then, he spoke. His voice was quiet.

'Where am I? I don't know where I am,' he said. 'Who are you?'

'You're in my valley – Burden Valley,' I said. 'You've been sick.'

I put the soup down near him.

'The valley,' he said. 'I remember now. I saw green trees. But there was no one in the valley.'

I didn't tell him about my secret cave.

'I'm here,' I said. 'I saw you were sick. I came to help you.'

'Sick,' he said. 'Yes, very sick.'

'I've made you some soup,' I said. 'Try to eat it.'

He tried to eat some of the soup. But he was too ill. I had to feed him.

Then he said, 'No more soup. I'm too sick.'

He went to sleep again. I touched his face. It was very hot.

I went back to the cave and got my clock, a lamp and this notebook.

———

This morning, he was much better. I took him some breakfast.

'Thank you,' he said. Then he sat up.

'What made me sick?' he asked. 'I must find out.'

'You went in Burden Creek,' I replied.

'What's Burden Creek?' he asked.

'It's the stream across the road,' I said. 'It's dangerous. Nothing lives in it. It's radioactive.'

He gave me his Geiger counter. 'Take this to the stream,' he said, 'and test the water.'

I went to the stream and held the Geiger counter above the water. The counter showed one hundred and eighty.

I went back to the tent and told the man.

'One hundred and eighty!' he said. 'And I was in the water for ten minutes. I have radiation sickness – very bad radiation sickness.'

'But you're getting better,' I said.

'No, you don't understand,' he replied. 'I studied radioactivity before the war. I know about radiation sickness. First, the person is sick. The sickness lasts for a day or two. Next comes the fever. The person is very hot. He cannot think clearly. I'm going to have the fever soon. Then I will be very, very ill.'

'How ill will you be?' I asked.

'I don't know,' he said. 'Perhaps I'll die. Perhaps I won't.'

7

John R Loomis

29th May. The man is in the house. He sleeps in my brother's room. I can look after him inside the house.

His name is John R Loomis. He told me yesterday. He's a scientist from Ithaca, New York. That's where Cornell University was before the war.

I woke up early. I felt happy. I knew there was someone to talk to.

I heated some water on the fire and had a bath. Then I put on clean clothes.

I went out to the chickens to get some eggs. When I came back, Mr Loomis was sitting up in bed.

'You're better,' I said.

'Yes,' he said. 'I'm better this morning, but the fever will start soon. I want to eat something, before I feel ill again.'

I gave him a large breakfast of eggs, bread and coffee.

He looked very surprised.

'Did you cook that yourself?' he said. 'Do you live here alone?'

'Yes,' I said. I didn't like answering his questions. 'I look after the farm alone. I work very hard. I have chickens and cows. There are fish in the river and I grow things in the fields.'

'Why hasn't the radioactivity killed everything in the valley?' he asked.

'I don't know,' I replied. 'People said the valley has different weather. The radioactivity never reached here.'

He ate his breakfast. Then he said, 'What's your name?'

I told him. 'Ann Burden,' I said.

'Were there many people living in the valley?' he asked.

'There was my family,' I said. 'And our neighbours. They all went to the nearest town. They took two trucks, but they didn't come back. They're dead.'

'Perhaps the gas killed them,' he said. 'The gas came after the bombs. When people breathed the gas, they went to sleep. They never woke up.'

'How long did it take you to come here?' I asked.

'About ten weeks,' he said. 'During that time, I saw nothing alive. No people, no animals, no birds, no trees. Everything was dead.'

Mr Loomis was ill and very tired. 'I'll have to rest,' he said. Soon, he was asleep.

I went down to the field by the pond. I moved the cows to another field. Then I milked them.

When I came back to the house, Mr Loomis was awake. I cooked some food. Then the man went on with his story.

'I was working at Cornell University,' he said. 'I was finding out more about plastics.'

Mr Loomis stopped for a moment.

'We were working for the government,' he said. 'Our work was secret. We were working in a secret place, under the ground. We were making a new kind of plastic. The plastic protected people from radiation. The Army wanted suits made of the new plastic.'

'But what about air?' I asked. 'How did the soldiers breathe?'

'We made another plastic,' he said. 'When radioactive air went through the plastic, the air was safe to breathe. The plastic made water safe, too.'

Now I understood. Mr Loomis's suit was made of plastic. The case on his back cleaned the air.

'The government wanted a lot of safe-suits,' said Mr Loomis. 'But there was no time to make them. When the war started, there was only one suit. But we were safe, under the ground. We had lots of food and water.'

'Were you under the ground when the bombs exploded?' I asked.

'Yes,' he said. 'We were in one of the safest places in the United States.'

'Are there other people alive?' I asked.

'Perhaps,' he said. 'If they are under the ground. But they must have food and water. They can't go outside, because of the radiation. They haven't got safe-suits. When their food and water has gone, they will die.'

'Did you try to find other people?' I asked.

'Yes,' he said. 'I took food and water with me. I found dead bodies everywhere.'

I gave Mr Loomis a cup of water. Then I remembered what he had said the other day.

'Who was Edward?' I asked quietly.

He dropped the cup and it fell to the floor.

'How do you know about Edward?' he asked.

'You called me Edward, yesterday,' I said. 'I went to see you in the tent. You were dreaming. You thought I was Edward.'

'Edward,' he said. 'Yes. Edward worked with me. He worked for the government.'

8

My New Friend

3rd June. Four days have passed. On 30 May, Mr Loomis was very ill again. His body was dry and hot. He shouted out when he was asleep.

'Can I get you some medicine?' I asked. 'There is some in the store.'

'No,' he replied. 'I have radiation sickness. The medicine in the store will not help me.'

On 31st May, I had a lot of work to do, so I left him. I went to the store and got some food. I'm also going to plant a lot of vegetables. I like fresh vegetables.

I got a spade and went to the garden. Soon I was digging.

Faro, the dog, came to watch me. The sun was very hot.

After a few hours, I looked up and saw Mr Loomis. I was worried. Why wasn't he in bed? I walked over to him.

'Is something wrong?' I asked.

'Nothing,' he said. 'I didn't want to stay in bed. It's very hot in the house. So I came outside. What are you doing?'

'I've been digging,' I replied. 'I'm going to plant some vegetables.'

'It's hard work for a girl,' he said. 'Didn't your father have a tractor?'

'Yes,' I said. 'But there's no petrol.'

'But there are two petrol pumps at the store,' he said. 'I'm sure they're not empty.'

'There is petrol at the store,' I said. 'But the pumps won't work without electricity.'

'We can work the pumps by hand,' Mr Loomis said. 'Then we'll have more than twenty thousand litres of petrol.'

It was getting dark. We walked back to the house together. He put his hand on my shoulder. I was pleased. He wanted me to help him. Soon he would be well.

After dinner, I made a fire in the living-room. It was cold outside, so I closed the windows. Mr Loomis didn't go to bed at once. He sat down in a chair and looked at the fire.

'I'm sorry, the electric lights don't work,' I said. 'There's no electricity. And I can't play any records.'

'Can you play the piano?' he asked.

'Not very well,' I said, 'but I'll try.'

I put an oil-lamp near the piano. Then I played the piano for him.

When I looked at him again, he had fallen asleep.

I stopped playing the piano and he woke up.

'That was beautiful,' he said, 'I haven't heard music for more than a year.'

Then he looked at me angrily. 'I'm sick,' he said. 'I'm ill again. I must go to bed.'

I was not tired now. I sat by the fire and read a book. It was an old book. Someone had given it to me when I was a child. There was a different letter of the alphabet on each page. The first page said *A is for Adam*. There was a picture of a man called Adam on the page. The next page said *B for Benjamin*. The last page in the book said *Z for Zachariah*.

Adam was the first man in the world. Perhaps Zachariah is the last man in the world.

Then I remembered Mr Loomis. Perhaps he is the last man in the world.

I like Mr Loomis. But sometimes, I'm frightened of him.

I was tired. I decided to go to bed. Then I heard Mr Loomis shout. He was talking loudly in his sleep. He was talking to Edward in his dream. Mr Loomis was very, very angry.

I got up and walked towards the door of his room.

'What good can it do?' Mr Loomis was shouting. 'We know they're dead. They're all dead. Can't you understand, Edward? Mary's dead. Billy's dead. You can't help them.'

Mr Loomis was quiet, and then he shouted again.

'Get away! Get away from – '

I didn't understand the last word. Mr Loomis was very ill again.

I decided to leave my bedroom door open. Perhaps Mr Loomis will want help during the night.

I lay down on the bed. Faro, the dog, came and lay down next to me.

9

I Dream of Marriage

I woke up very early on 1st June. I had had a dream during the night. It was about my mother. I got out of bed quickly and walked downstairs. I stood outside Mr Loomis's bedroom door. There was no sound. Mr Loomis was asleep.

I walked out into the fields. I wanted to get some green plants to eat. The air was fresh and clean. The grass in the field was long and wet. Soon my jeans were wet too. There were fish swimming in the pond. I felt happy. Faro was with me. He saw a rabbit and ran after it. I didn't have my gun with me so the rabbit got away. Faro wasn't very pleased.

As I walked with Faro, I thought about my life.

Next June, I'll be seventeen years old. Perhaps I'll get married when I'm seventeen. Mr Loomis is ill now. But perhaps he'll want to marry me later. My seventeenth birthday will be the best day for the wedding.

I dreamt about a wedding at the church. I'll wear my mother's wedding dress, I thought. There'll be lots of flowers. In ten years' time, I'll have children.

Before the war, I had had a boy-friend. We were both thirteen. He invited me to a dance at our school. The parents went to the dance too. They sat and watched their children. I didn't enjoy the dance.

Will Mr Loomis want to marry me?

I decided to get him some flowers. Then I went back to the house.

The house was quiet. I cooked Mr Loomis's breakfast and knocked on his door. There was no answer. Then I looked through the window. He was outside, by the Creek. He was sitting on a large, round stone.

He had his Geiger counter with him. He saw me and walked back towards the house.

'Are you all right?' I asked him.

'Yes,' he said. 'I felt better when I woke up. I came to test the water again.'

'What did the counter show?' I asked.

'It's bad, very bad,' he said. 'The radioactivity in the water is very strong. I'm not sure if I'll live.'

Then Mr Loomis told me his plans about electricity. He wanted electricity in Burden Valley!

'This water is radioactive,' he said. 'But it can be useful. I'm going to build a dam. I will build the dam across the Creek. It will keep the water in the Creek. I've found an old electric motor. I can make a machine from it. The moving water will make the machine go. Then we can have electricity.'

'But it's too dangerous to go in the water,' I said.

'No,' said Mr Loomis. 'I'll wear the safe-suit. When the machine is ready, we can have electric lights. The refrigerator and the freezer will work too.'

After breakfast, I milked the cows and planted some vegetables.

Then Mr Loomis called me. 'I feel very sick again,' he said. 'It's the sixth day of my illness. The radiation is in my blood.'

I helped him back to his bedroom. Then I went fishing. I caught three fish in the pond.

Mr Loomis was asleep when I went back to the house. I put a cup of water by his bed. I hoped he'd be better soon.

That evening, Mr Loomis was better again. I made a fire and cooked the fish. I cut up the green plants and put everything on the table. It was dark outside, but the house was warm and comfortable.

Mr Loomis got up for dinner and we ate the meal together. Then he read my father's book about farm pumps and machines. I know we're going to have electricity soon.

10

The Tractor

The next day was 2nd June. When I had cooked the breakfast, I took the food to Mr Loomis. He was awake. He was looking at one of my father's books.

'Look at this,' said Mr Loomis.

He showed me a drawing of a petrol pump. It was the same as the pump at the store.

'Although there is no electricity, we can get the petrol,' he said. 'Inside the pump there is a handle. If you turn the handle a few times, the petrol will come out.'

I left him in bed and went to the store. I found the handle in the pump. I turned it once, twice, three times.

Petrol! At last, I had petrol for the tractor!

Two hours later, I had filled the tractor's petrol tank. It was difficult to start the tractor. It hadn't been used for a long time. But at last, it was going again! The noise of the motor was very loud.

I climbed up to the seat and drove the tractor to the house. I was very happy! My tractor will save me a lot of work.

I was very excited, but Mr Loomis wasn't.

'I knew we could get the petrol out,' he said.

I drove the tractor out to the fields. It was a beautiful day. The sun felt warm on my back. Faro ran round and round the tractor. Soon the tractor was turning over the earth in the field.

After lunch, I wanted to work in another field. But Mr Loomis was very ill and I didn't want to leave him. Sometimes he was too hot. Sometimes he was too cold. He was afraid to be alone.

That evening, I cooked him a big dinner. I cooked a chicken and lots of vegetables.

'I don't want to eat,' he said. 'I'm not hungry.'

I went back to the dining-room and left him in his bedroom. I was hungry. I had worked hard all morning.

'Ann,' he shouted. 'Come here!'

I went back to the bedroom. Mr Loomis looked terrible.

'I feel very, very cold,' he said. But his face was hot and wet.

'Try to sleep,' I said. 'I'll get you another blanket.'

'You're kind to me,' he said. 'Thank you.'

I was worried. Mr Loomis had a very bad fever. I didn't know how to look after him. And there were so many other things to do.

I sat near Mr Loomis for many hours. I held his hand. Was he going to die? I was very frightened. I did not want to live alone.

———

This morning, I got up early. I drove the tractor to the stream. We needed some more water. Then I drove quickly back to the house.

I was only one hundred metres from the house, when Mr Loomis came out. It was difficult for him to walk. He was shouting and his face looked very strange. Faro saw him and ran away.

Slowly, Mr Loomis moved towards his wagon. He opened the cover and put his hand inside. He took out his gun, then he turned and pointed the gun at the house. He fired three times. I saw three big holes in the wooden wall of the house.

'Edward!' he shouted. 'Where are you? Edward, Edward!'

I held Mr Loomis's arm. 'You're dreaming again,' I said. 'Go back to bed. You'll feel better tomorrow.'

I helped him into bed. He didn't know I was there.

I'm worried. Why did Mr Loomis want to kill Edward?

11

Edward

Morning, 4th June. This is a terrible day. I think Mr Loomis is dying.

He sleeps a lot, but he has frightening dreams. When he's awake, he doesn't see me or hear me.

Mr Loomis is very frightened. He talks all the time about one man – Edward. He thinks Edward is here. He's always shouting Edward's name. I don't understand. Mr Loomis and Edward were friends. Then something happened. Now Mr Loomis and Edward are enemies.

Sometimes Mr Loomis thinks I'm Edward. Sometimes he thinks he is working with Edward. Sometimes he thinks Edward is here, in Burden Valley.

I took Mr Loomis his breakfast this morning. He was awake, but in a dream. He spoke. I know he wasn't talking to me.

'Don't come near, Edward,' he said. 'Don't come near.'

'Mr Loomis,' I said. 'It's me. I've brought you some breakfast.'

'No breakfast. I'm too sick,' he said.

'Try to drink something,' I said. 'I've brought you a cold drink.'

I held out the glass and he took it.

'I'll bring you some more later,' I said. 'Now try to eat.'

'Edward? Edward!' he said.

'Mr Loomis,' I said, 'Edward isn't here.'

'I know,' he replied. 'Where did he go?'

'You mustn't worry about him,' I said.

'You don't understand,' Mr Loomis said. 'Edward wants it. He'll try to take the – '

Mr Loomis tried to get out of bed. I held his shoulders and stopped him. Then he lay quietly. He was breathing very quickly.

'The suit,' he said quietly. 'The safe-suit. He'll take the safe-suit!'

Now I know the truth. Mr Loomis is afraid that Edward will take the safe-suit.

'Mr Loomis,' I said. 'The suit's in the wagon. You put it there. Can't you remember?'

———

Afternoon. I got the suit and put it in Mr Loomis's bedroom. Mr Loomis was dreaming about Edward again. In this dream, they were both shouting at each other.

'. . . No, Edward,' said Mr Loomis. 'You can't have it for twenty-four hours. You can't have it. I'm keeping it. The suit must stay here. You can go out, but you can't come back. The door will be locked!'

Now I understood the story. After the war, Edward and Mr Loomis were working together. They were under the ground when the bombs exploded. And so they were alive. But Edward was married. He wanted to go home and look for his wife and son.

Outside, everything was radioactive. There was only one safe-suit. But two men wanted it. Edward had taken the suit and put it on.

'Take off that suit and give it to me,' shouted Mr Loomis. 'If

you don't take it off, I'll shoot you. The suit will stop radiation, but it won't stop bullets.'

I walked over to the chair. I looked carefully at the safe-suit. There were three new pieces of plastic on the front of the suit. Mr Loomis had shot Edward three times. Then he had repaired the suit.

Now I'm sure that Mr Loomis killed Edward.

I went to the church. I wanted to pray. I prayed for Mr Loomis. I prayed for him to live. I know Mr Loomis has killed a man. But I don't want him to die.

I hope he won't kill me.

12

Mr Loomis Wakes Up

7th June. Mr Loomis has been in bed for several days. He looks better today. He's asleep. He has a fever but his breathing is quieter.

I'm going to put clean sheets on Mr Loomis's bed. There's a lot of washing to do. I don't want to be a nurse. I want to be a teacher. I don't like looking after sick people.

When I had done the washing, I sat down. I was tired and wanted to rest. I thought about the safe-suit. Then I thought about the library in Ogdentown. I like reading. Ogdentown isn't far away, but the radioactivity is there.

Perhaps I can take the safe-suit? If I am wearing the safe-suit, I can go into Ogdentown. I can bring some books back here. But I hope the books won't be radioactive.

Then I remembered Edward . . .

15th June. It's my birthday today. I'm sixteen years old. Mr Loomis woke up this morning. He's better, but he's very, very thin. But he must eat some food, and then I know he'll live.

Today, we had chicken, vegetables and a cake for dinner. Mr Loomis couldn't walk, so I put the food on a table by his bed.

'I can't believe it,' he said. 'Last week I thought I was dying. Now I am eating again.'

___

16th June. Today he ate more food. He stayed awake longer too. I'm not so worried about him now. I don't have to stay in the house with him. I can work in the garden. I have a lot of work to do in the garden.

I am pleased Mr Loomis is getting better. But he is often angry. He makes me frightened. When I gave him his breakfast this morning, he asked me many questions.

'Have you planted all the vegetables?' he asked.

I told him how much work I had done.

'What did you do when I was ill?' he asked. 'Where did you go?'

'I went to church,' I said.

'To church,' he said. 'Why did you go there? How long were you there? Why didn't you work in the fields?'

I did not want to answer. Before Mr Loomis came to my valley, I was free. I could do what I liked. I helped him when he was ill. Now he thinks my valley is his.

He tries to walk. Sometimes he falls, and I help him back to bed. But soon he'll be strong again. He'll be stronger than me. I hope he'll be kind to me.

13

Mr Loomis Makes Plans

22nd June. Mr Loomis can walk again. At first, he had to hold on to the table and chairs. Now he can walk easily. He is eating and sleeping well. He is much stronger.

This morning, Mr Loomis was awake early. He started to write and draw in a notebook. He was drawing a machine. The machine is going to make electricity. He is going to build the machine in the Creek. The water in the Creek will make the machine go.

'I want some books,' he said.

'What books?' I asked.

'Books about electricity and machines,' he said. 'Have you got any?'

'No,' I said. 'But there are some books in the library in Ogdentown.'

'How far is Ogdentown from here?' Mr Loomis asked.

'About thirty kilometres,' I replied.

I waited for a few seconds.

'Will the books in Ogdentown library be radioactive?' I said. 'Will they be dangerous?'

'Yes, they will,' he said.

'When will they be safe?' I asked.

'It'll be six months before we can read them here,' he said. 'But that's not important. I'll put on the safe-suit. I'll go to Ogdentown. I can read the books in the library.'

'I want to read some books too,' I said. 'There are lots of stories in the library. Let me wear the suit. I'll walk to Ogdentown.'

Mr Loomis got very, very angry. 'No,' he said. 'You can

never have the suit. Keep away from the suit. Don't touch it!'

I remembered what had happened to Edward. I was frightened and said nothing.

Mr Loomis looked at me in a strange way.

'My suit is the most important thing in the world,' he said. 'I cannot go outside the valley without it.'

I was sad. I wanted some books to read at home. But I didn't say anything. I was frightened of Mr Loomis.

Mr Loomis is stronger now. He sits outside during the day. He watches me work in the garden and in the fields. He tells me what to do. But he does not help me.

I don't understand Mr Loomis. He never talks about himself. One evening, I wanted to ask him some questions. I sat down beside him. I asked him about his family and his work.

But his answers were very short. I asked him if he had been married. He looked at me in a strange way. Then he spoke quietly.

'I thought you were going to ask me that question,' he said.

Suddenly, he held my left hand. I was very surprised. I could not move away. He held my hand strongly, in both his hands.

'No,' he said. 'I never got married. Why did you ask that?'

I didn't answer. I didn't know what to say.

Mr Loomis pulled me closer towards him. I tried to get away, but I couldn't.

'Why did you ask if I was married?' he said again.

'Please let me go,' I said. I felt very unhappy. I did not know what to do and I was frightened.

My hand was hard and dry. I had been working in the fields all day. Mr Loomis's hands were soft, but very strong.

I did not know what to do. Mr Loomis was pulling me out of my chair. I was falling towards him.

I was frightened. Mr Loomis was not smiling.

'Answer me first,' he said.

'I asked because I was interested,' I said.

He pulled me closer to him. 'Interested in what?' he asked.

I was falling, falling . . . my right hand hit Mr Loomis's face.

Mr Loomis let me go. I got up quickly from my chair.

'Why did you do that?' he said quietly.

'I'm sorry,' I said. 'I was falling.'

Mr Loomis smiled. 'You held my hand when I was ill,' he said.

I did not speak. I ran into the kitchen.

14

I Leave Mr Loomis

30th June. I'm living in the cave again. Mr Loomis doesn't know where the cave is. I didn't want to come here, but I cannot live in the house with Mr Loomis. I'm terribly frightened of him. Something has happened. I will never sleep in the house again.

On 25th June, I got up early. I fed the animals and worked in the fields for three hours. Then I went back to the house and cooked breakfast for Mr Loomis. After that, I went back to work in the fields again.

I knew he was watching me. Mr Loomis sat outside the house all day. But I didn't look at him.

That evening, Mr Loomis came into the kitchen. I had finished cooking the supper.

'I don't want to eat in bed,' he said. 'I'm well again. I'll eat my supper with you.'

I put the food on the table and we sat down. He sat at one end of the table and I sat at the other end.

After supper, Mr Loomis lit two oil-lamps.

'Why don't you read to me?' he said.

I didn't want to read to Mr Loomis. But I didn't want him to be angry. I read to him for more than an hour. I don't think he was listening to me. But he sat quietly.

————

The next night, he asked me to play the piano. I sat at the piano and he sat in a chair behind me. I could not see Mr Loomis and I was worried.

I played the piano for a long time. I didn't play well. I was very tired.

'I'm sorry,' I said. 'I can't play any more. I'm too tired.'

'Why are you tired?' Mr Loomis asked.

'I've been working all day,' I said.

'There's a lot of work,' he said. 'We must grow enough food for next year. Soon, I will be able to help you. You must teach me how to use the tractor.'

————

The next day, I cooked supper early. It was a quiet, warm evening. After supper, Mr Loomis went to his room. I decided to go for a walk with Faro. We walked slowly down the road to the church.

On the way back to the house, I stopped by the pond. I saw something moving near the house. It was Mr Loomis. He was looking inside the wagon. Then he turned and looked along the road. But he didn't see me. Mr Loomis walked quickly back to the house. I could see he was much stronger now. He was walking well.

I went quietly into the house. Mr Loomis had gone to his room. The house was dark.

I went up to my bedroom. I took off my shoes and lay down on the bed. Faro came and sat near me. Soon I was asleep.

I woke up in the middle of the night. It was very, very dark. Faro was making a noise. Why had he woken up? Then I knew.

Mr Loomis was in the room. He was breathing loudly. I didn't move or speak. Perhaps he'll go away, I thought.

But he moved towards me, very slowly and very quietly. I knew he was near the bed.

Suddenly, both his hands were touching me. His breathing got faster and louder. He touched my face.

I moved quickly, away from him. I fell off the bed and onto the floor. Then I got up and ran.

15

Hiding in the Cave

I got out of the house, and ran and ran. I was very, very frightened. I thought Mr Loomis was following me. I ran down the road until I reached the store. I was breathing very quickly. I couldn't run further. I was cold. I had left my shoes in the house.

Mr Loomis hadn't followed me and I couldn't see Faro. I

decided to go to the cave. I would be safe there. I took some things from the store and walked slowly to the cave.

I didn't sleep again that night. I sat in front of the cave and watched the house.

When it was light, I picked up my binoculars. I looked at the house. I saw Faro first. He came out of the house and walked round Mr Loomis's tent. The dog walked slowly. He was smelling the ground with his nose. I knew he was trying to find me.

Mr Loomis came to the door of the house. He looked at Faro. He knew Faro was trying to find me. He watched Faro very carefully.

Soon, Faro went behind the trees near the house. Mr Loomis went back inside the house. I knew he couldn't see my cave. There are too many trees in front of it.

Ten minutes later, Faro was standing outside the cave. I was pleased to see him. But I did something wrong. I didn't feed Faro.

When Faro was hungry, he went back to the house. Mr Loomis put some food in the garden for the dog. Faro was hungry and started to eat. Then Mr Loomis took a rope and tied it round Faro's neck. He tied the other end of the rope to the gate.

Poor Faro! No one had tied him up with a rope before. At first, he tried to run away. Then he tried to bite the rope. All the time, Mr Loomis was watching him. Soon Faro stopped pulling on the rope. Mr Loomis smiled and went into the house.

Today is 1st July. Faro was tied to the rope all day yesterday. In the evening, Mr Loomis came outside with some food. But he didn't give it to Faro at once. First, he untied the rope from the gate. Then, holding the rope, he walked down the road, behind the dog.

Faro knew what to do. He walked along smelling the ground. He was trying to find me. After a few metres, they walked back to the house. Then Mr Loomis gave Faro the food.

After a few minutes, Mr Loomis walked slowly down the road towards the store. He went inside. When he came out of the store, he looked up at the hills round the valley. But he could not see me. So he went back to the house.

Last night, I thought about Mr Loomis. I thought about my farm and my valley. I decided to talk to Mr Loomis.

This morning, I went down to the house. I stood on the road, outside the house. When Mr Loomis saw me, he came out.

'So, you're back,' he said.

'I'm not coming back,' I said.

'But why not?' he asked. 'Where will you stay?'

'I'll find somewhere to stay,' I replied.

'Why did you come back?' Mr Loomis asked.

'I don't want to live with you,' I said. 'But we both live in the valley. We must look after the animals and grow food. I'll work, and you can work too. I'll bring you food until you are stronger. You can cook it yourself. But leave me alone.'

Mr Loomis looked at me for a long time. But he said nothing. He went back into the house.

I decided to go on working. I worked in the garden. I looked after the chickens and the animals. I brought Mr Loomis food and water. But every night, I returned to my secret cave.

I was lonely before Mr Loomis came to the valley. But he's a

47

bad man. I don't like him. Perhaps there are other valleys like mine. Perhaps there are other people in the world.

I think I'll go away. I'll try to find another valley. I'll leave Mr Loomis here.

16

Mr Loomis Tries to Kill Me

4th August (*I think*). I don't know what to do. Mr Loomis has shot me. I haven't written in my notebook for a long time. I have been too ill and too afraid.

After I had spoken to Mr Loomis, I went on working. Every day, I worked in the fields. I took Mr Loomis some food. I went to the house a different way every day.

Mr Loomis can walk easily now. He can also drive the tractor. We both used the tractor and we both took food from the store. I took milk, eggs and vegetables from the farm too.

Living in the cave is more difficult than living in the house. It is cold at night. I have to walk a long way to the store.

Mr Loomis knew I often went to the store. He didn't like me going there. He didn't want me to drive the tractor. One day, he took the tractor key. I couldn't start the tractor without the key. Mr Loomis kept the key in his pocket.

I had lost my house, Faro the dog and the tractor. But I had the chickens, eggs and milk. There were some fish in the pond and vegetables in the garden. I was never hungry.

Then Mr Loomis decided to catch me. He thought I lived in the store.

One afternoon, I saw him come out of the house. I watched him through the binoculars. He had his gun in one hand. He

48

held Faro's rope in the other hand. He took Faro with him to the tractor.

Mr Loomis tied Faro's rope to the tractor and started the engine. Then he drove off towards the store. Faro followed him.

Mr Loomis stopped the tractor near the store. He stood and watched for a minute or two. Then, holding the gun in both hands, he moved towards the store. Mr Loomis wanted to shoot me!

He was in the store for a long time. He looked in every room. When he came out again, he looked angry.

Then he locked the door of the store and put the key in his pocket. He smiled and drove the tractor back to the house.

Now I had lost my house, Faro, the tractor and the store.

——

Next morning, I woke up very early. I put my blanket with the other things in the cave and cooked my breakfast.

I thought about the store. There were many things I wanted.

I must be strong, I thought. I'll go and ask Mr Loomis for the key to the store.

I went down the hill and stood in front of the house.

'Mr Loomis!' I shouted.

At first, nothing happened. Then there was a loud noise, and a pain in my right leg.

Mr Loomis had shot me!

I looked up and saw Mr Loomis. He was in one of the bedrooms. He was pointing a gun out of the window. I turned and ran down the road. Bang! A bullet from the gun hit the road behind me.

A few seconds later, I was hiding near some trees. I stopped running and looked at my leg. There were two holes in my jeans. But the bullet wasn't in my leg. There was a small hole and some blood.

17

I Kill Faro

I went to the pond. I wanted to wash my leg. Why had Mr Loomis shot me? Did he want to kill me? But then I understood. He had shot twice at my leg. He didn't want to kill me. He wanted to stop me running away. He had caught Faro. Now he wanted to catch me.

As I sat by the pond, I heard the tractor engine. Mr Loomis was driving back to the store with Faro. They were looking for me again. Mr Loomis stopped the tractor.

'Where is she, Faro?' Mr Loomis asked the dog.

Faro smelt the ground with his nose. Soon, he was pulling on the rope.

'Good dog!' said Mr Loomis. He was pleased. He followed Faro up the hill.

I knew Faro was going to my cave. I had to get there first. I got up and ran. I reached the cave before them.

Quickly, I put some food in a bag. I picked up my gun and ran higher up the hill. Then, I sat down and waited.

Faro and Mr Loomis soon found the cave. Mr Loomis pointed his gun into the cave.

'Come out!' he shouted.

He waited a few seconds. Then he went inside. A few seconds later, he came out. He was carrying my blanket, my books and all the other things from the cave. He put them together on the ground and burnt them.

Ten minutes later, Mr Loomis and Faro went back to the house. I sat and watched the smoke go up in the air. I wanted to cry.

———

6th August. It's raining. I'm sitting under a tree. My leg's nearly better. I've made a plan. I can't live in the valley. I won't live near Mr Loomis.

I'm going to take the safe-suit. I'm going to leave the valley.

I want to find a new home. I want to live with good, kind people. Perhaps I can find some children to teach. I've always wanted to be a teacher.

Mr Loomis came from the north. Nothing was alive there. The bombs and the gas had killed everything. I'll go south. There are lots of valleys to the south. Perhaps there are other people alive.

I'll need the safe-suit, the tent, the wagon, my gun and the binoculars. I'll put some food and water in the wagon, too.

I've thought about my plan, carefully. Soon, I'll be ready.

———

Evening. Something terrible happened to Faro this afternoon.

I was getting some fruit from some plants on the hill. I pulled the fruit off the plants and ate it. I looked down at the store in the valley. Mr Loomis had left the door of the store open! I thought he had forgotten to lock it.

I started walking towards the store. Suddenly, I stopped. I

was about forty metres from the store. Something moved inside the store, near the window.

Mr Loomis was waiting for me. He was hiding in the store. He fired his gun at me from the window of the store.

I turned and ran back up the hill. I went to the tree and got my gun. I could hear Faro and Mr Loomis following me. They were coming through the trees.

I ran and ran. Soon, I came to the Creek.

I must not touch the water. It'll kill me, I thought.

But I had to get across the water. There were some big rocks in the Creek. I jumped from one rock to another. I didn't touch the water. A minute later, I was safe on the other side of the Creek.

I hid behind the large rock and waited.

Soon, Mr Loomis and Faro reached the Creek. I took my gun and pointed it above Mr Loomis's head. I wanted to frighten him.

I fired the gun. Mr Loomis was surprised. He let go of Faro's rope. Then he turned and ran back towards the house.

Faro ran towards the Creek. But he didn't know about the radioactive water. He went straight into the water and began to move towards me.

Poor Faro! I know he will be very ill. He will get sick like Mr Loomis.

18

I Leave Burden Valley

7th August. I am waiting for Mr Loomis. Last night, I slept in the valley for the last time. Faro slept beside me. He was sick, very early in the morning. Before it was light, he was dead. I was very sad. My only friend in the world was dead.

I carried Faro's body to the top of the hill. I covered it with stones.

I had decided what to do. I was going to take the safe-suit and leave the valley. I went down towards the house. It was still dark and everything was quiet.

I went quietly up to the house. I had written a note for Mr Loomis. I had thought about the words carefully. This is what I had written:

I'm not going to hide any more. Come to the south end of the valley. We can talk there.

I left the note outside the door and walked back up the hill. I sat and watched the house. I did not wait long. Mr Loomis came out of the house. He saw the note immediately. A few minutes later, he was walking towards the south end of the valley.

I ran quickly, towards the house. I went up to the wagon. I lifted the green, plastic cover and looked inside. Everything was there – the safe-suit, food, water and the air tank. The Geiger counter and the tent were there, too.

I pulled the wagon down the road. It was mine. And Mr Loomis's safe-suit was mine, too.

I put on the safe-suit. Soon, I was walking towards the dead, radioactive world. The wagon moved quietly behind me. I was leaving my beautiful valley.

When I reached the end of the valley, I stopped. I put on the air tank. Then I walked forward into the polluted, radioactive world.

Mr Loomis will wait at the south end of the valley. But I will not meet him there. Soon, he will understand what I have done. He'll go back to the house. He'll see I have taken the wagon. Then, he'll come and find me. But he has no protection against radiation. I'll wait for him here. He cannot touch me or take away the safe-suit here.

———

8th August. In the early morning, I heard the tractor. Mr Loomis was driving very fast. When he got near me, he stopped. In front of him was the dead, radioactive land and I was standing in it. He was not able to come any nearer. He was holding his gun. Was he going to shoot me?

'Drop your gun,' I said.

'Give me the safe-suit. It's mine!' he shouted.

'No,' I said. 'I won't.'

He pointed his gun at me.

'Go on,' I said. 'Kill me. You killed Edward. Now kill me.'

Mr Loomis looked at me for a long time. 'No, no,' he said. Then, he put down his gun. 'How did you know that I killed Edward?' he said.

'You told me when you were ill,' I said. 'You told me why you shot him.' I pointed to the front of the suit. 'The bullets went here,' I said.

At first, he said nothing. He stood quietly. Then he spoke.

'Edward tried to take my suit,' he said. 'Now you're taking it.'

'I have to,' I said. 'I don't want to die. I can't live in the valley with you. I'm going to look for a new home. I want to live with good people. If you want to stop me, you'll have to kill me.'

'No,' he said. 'You're wrong.'

He looked at me again.

'Don't go,' he said. 'Don't leave me here alone.'

'You tried to kill me,' I said. 'I'm going to leave you.

Perhaps I'll find other people. I'll tell them about you. Perhaps they'll come and see you. You have food, the tractor and the store. The valley is yours.'

I looked at my valley for the last time. Slowly, I breathed the clean air from the air tank. I began to pull the wagon.

I heard Mr Loomis shouting. At first, I couldn't hear the words clearly. I turned and looked at him. He was pointing to the west and shouting the same words again and again.

'Birds,' he said. 'I saw birds. When I walked here, I saw birds flying in the west. Perhaps there is another valley . . .'

Then I turned away from Mr Loomis, and walked away from the valley.

Points for Understanding

INTRODUCTION

1 How long did the war last?
2 What kind of bombs exploded?
3 How many people died when the bombs exploded?
4 Some people did not die at once. They tried to live in the pollution. What illness did these people die of?

1

1 Ann Burden was fifteen years old when the war started. How old is she now?
2 Where does Ann live?
3 What happened to her parents?
4 Ann's valley has green trees and grass. She can drink the water in one of the streams. The air is pure. What is the land outside the valley like?

2

1 Ann's father took Joseph and David to Ogdentown. What did they find there?
2 The next day, Ann's father went to Dean Town. Who went with him?
3 Why did Ann stay on the farm?
4 Ann writes about her family on 20th May.
   (a) When did her family leave the valley?
   (b) How long has Ann been alone?
5 Ann thinks someone is coming to her valley. Why?

3

1 Ann decided to put some food and clothes in a secret place. What is this secret place?
2 Ann sees the person coming to her valley.
   (a) How can she see the person clearly?
   (b) What is the person wearing?
   (c) What is the person pulling?

4

1 Where was Ann hiding when the man came into the valley? *in a cave*
2 The man went to his wagon and took out two instruments. What did he do with the first instrument?
3 The second instrument was a Geiger counter. What did he use the Geiger counter for?
4 The man called out, 'Is anyone here?' Why did Ann not reply?
5 The man took off his mask. What did he look like?
6 Where did the man sleep that night?
7 In the morning, the man went to the store. When he came out he made a terrible mistake. What was the mistake?

5

1 What strange thing happened in the afternoon?
2 On 26th May, the man went to the store again. When he came out he looked different. x
   (a) What did he look like?
   (b) How old did Ann think he was?
3 The man walked to the south end of the valley. He saw that there were two streams. Why was he worried?

6

1 On 27th May, the man did not feed Faro. Why?
2 What did Ann see when she looked inside the tent?
3 'What made me sick?' the man asked. What did Ann reply?
4 The man gave Ann the Geiger counter. What did he want her to do?
5 The man said he had radiation sickness. Why did he know a lot about radiation sickness?
6 What happens to someone who has radiation sickness?

7

1 Where was the man sleeping on 29th May?
2 What was the man's name?
3 What was the man's job?

4 Where did he come from?
5 The man had been working on a new kind of plastic. Who wanted suits made out of the plastic?
6 They also made a plastic case. What did the plastic case do?
7 Why was the man safe when the bombs exploded?
8 Who was Edward?

8

1 The next time Ann wrote in the notebook, the date was 3rd June.
  (a) Why had Ann not written before?
  (b) How many days had passed?
2 Why did Ann go to dig in the garden?
3 'There is petrol at the store,' Ann said. 'But the pumps won't work without electricity.'
  (a) Mr Loomis said they could make the pumps work. How?
  (b) How much petrol did Mr Loomis think they would have?
4 What did Mr Loomis ask Ann to do after dinner?

9

1 Early on 31st May, Ann went into the fields. What did she think might happen next June?
2 What did Ann think she would have in ten years' time?
3 Where was Mr Loomis when Ann took him his breakfast?
4 What did he have with him?
5 How was Mr Loomis going to bring electricity to Burden Valley?

10

1 On 2nd June, Ann got the tractor going. What job did she do first?
2 Ann went on the tractor to get some water. Where was Mr Loomis when she got back to the house?
3 What did Mr Loomis take from the wagon?

11

1 Ann thought that Mr Loomis was dying.
    (a) What name did he call out many times?
    (b) Who did he think Ann was?
    (c) What was he afraid of?
2 Ann looked at the front of the suit. What did she see?
3 What did she know about Mr Loomis now?

12

1 Ann did not want to be a nurse. What job did she want?
2 Ann wanted to go to the library in Ogdentown. How did she think she could get some books?
3 'What did you do when I was ill?' Mr Loomis asked.
    (a) What did Ann reply?
    (b) Why did Ann not want to answer his questions?

13

1 Ann asked Mr Loomis if she could wear the safe-suit to Ogdentown.
    (a) What happened?
    (b) Why was Ann frightened?
2 One evening, Ann asked Mr Loomis if he was married. What did Mr Loomis do?
3 What happened when Ann fell?

14

1 Where was Ann when she wrote her notebook on 30th June?
2 Why was she there?
3 One evening, Ann had gone for a walk with Faro. When she came back, she saw Mr Loomis by the wagon. What did she notice about this?
4 Mr Loomis came into Ann's room. How did Ann escape?

15

1 Ann ran from the house.
   (a) Where did she go first?
   (b) Where did she go then?
2 Ann did not sleep that night. What did she do instead?
3 Mr Loomis gave Faro some food. What did he do when Faro started eating?
4 Faro walked along smelling the ground. What was Mr Loomis trying to make the dog do?
5 'I don't want to live with you,' Ann said. 'But we both live in the valley.' What did Ann say she would do until Mr Loomis was stronger?
6 Ann did not like Mr Loomis. What did she want to do?

16

1 One afternoon, Mr Loomis drove to the store. What did he do there?
2 What happened when Ann went to speak to him?

17

1 Why did Mr Loomis not want to kill Ann?
2 Mr Loomis used Faro to find Ann's secret cave. What did he do when he found it?
3 Ann made a plan. What was the plan?
4 Why did Ann jump from one rock to another in Burden Creek?
5 Why did Ann think Faro would be very ill?

18

1 Ann wrote to Mr Loomis. Where did she ask him to meet her?
2 Ann did not go to meet Mr Loomis. Where did she go?
3 Why did Ann want to leave the valley?
4 What were the last words Mr Loomis said?
5 Why were Mr Loomis's words important?

Road to Nowhere *by John Milne*
The Black Cat *by John Milne*
Don't Tell Me What To Do *by Michael Hardcastle*
The Runaways *by Victor Canning*
The Red Pony *by John Steinbeck*
The Goalkeeper's Revenge and Other Stories *by Bill Naughton*
The Stranger *by Norman Whitney*
The Promise *by R.L. Scott-Buccleuch*
The Man With No Name *by Evelyn Davies and Peter Town*
The Cleverest Person in the World *by Norman Whitney*
Claws *by John Landon*
Z for Zachariah *by Robert C. O'Brien*
Tales of Horror *by Bram Stoker*
Frankenstein *by Mary Shelley*
Silver Blaze and Other Stories *by Sir Arthur Conan Doyle*
Tales of Ten Worlds *by Arthur C. Clarke*
The Boy Who Was Afraid *by Armstrong Sperry*
Room 13 and Other Ghost Stories *by M.R. James*
The Narrow Path *by Francis Selormey*
The Woman in Black *by Susan Hill*

For further information on the full selection of
Readers at all five levels in the series, please refer to
the Heinemann Guided Readers catalogue.

Heinemann International
A division of Heinemann Publishers (Oxford) Ltd
Halley Court, Jordan Hill, Oxford OX2 8EJ

OXFORD LONDON EDINBURGH
MADRID ATHENS BOLOGNA PARIS
MELBOURNE SYDNEY AUCKLAND SINGAPORE TOKYO
IBADAN NAIROBI HARARE GABORONE
PORTSMOUTH (NH)

ISBN 0 435 27209 8

© Sally M. Conly 1975
First published by Victor Gollancz Ltd 1975
This retold version for Heinemann Guided Readers
© Peter Hodson 1982, 1992
First published 1982
Reprinted three times
This edition published 1992

Typography by Adrian Hodgkins
Cover by Phyllis Mahon and Threefold Design
Typeset in 11.5/14.5 pt Goudy
by Joshua Associates Ltd, Oxford
Printed and bound in Malta

92 93 94 95 96 97 10 9 8 7 6 5 4 3 2 1